# The Blessings Book

# *The Blessings Book*

## THE DAY IS RICH WITH BLESSINGS

© Lizzi Vandorpe

ISBN: 978-1-906316-20-4

Published by Word4Word in 2008.
8 King Charles Court, Evesham, Worcestershire.
www.w4wdp.com


Printed in the UK by TJ International, Padstow.

# The Blessings Book

## THE DAY IS RICH WITH BLESSINGS

Lizzi Vandorpe

*This book is dedicated to*

_____

*on date/in year*

_____

*by*

_____

*and further dedicated to*

_____

*on date/in year*

_____

*Personal Message:*

_____

_____

_____

_____

# Acknowledgements

For the deep prompt of my mothers voice in a dream at 5.30am on New Years Eve morning 2008. She reminded me that when faced with a time of worry, I should first turn my thoughts to the endless blessings that always surround me. By reaping that gratitude I have all the positive answers I need to overcome my concerns. Thanks Mum. I miss you.

For the support of my amazing friends, who have laughed and cried with me along the way and filled me with the encouragement to follow my dreams.

To Sue Richardson, Cara Carey and the team at Word4Word: I knew we were looking for someone special to produce **The Blessings Book**. I wanted it to feel like a hidden treasure. You have exceeded our expectations. Thank you!

I have included inspiring quotes from many wise and enlightened minds. For sharing that wisdom for the greater good of all, thank you.

To our children: through their eyes we can see more clearly. Thank you for listening and accepting the idea of **The Blessings Book**. You are all my blessings. We have so much to learn from your innocence, beauty and love.

En aan mijn knappe, vriendelijke, liefdevolle echtgenoot, bedankt!

## Introduction to The Blessings Book

Why is it that the modern media seems to only ever report bad news? How wonderful would it be if someone created a "Good News Paper" which contained only stories about the marvellous things that happened around the globe? With **The Blessings Book** you can!

## Make **The Blessings Book** yours!

**The Blessings Book** is for you to keep a record of all those special moments... the many positive and wonderful daily things that we can easily miss unless we take a moment to stop and reflect on them.

Throughout this book there are pages left blank for your own entries along with quotes that you may recognise as blessings that perhaps exist in your own world.

## Reflection!

When we look at an old photo, we immediately relive a captured experience.

Your entries into **The Blessings Book** will capture a moment in time that was kind, or happy, or loving. Just by opening this little book, you will be reminded of wonderful news, which you can reflect on and enjoy time and time again.

A blessing can be as simple as taking time to catch up with an old friend or an unexpected kindness from a stranger. Blessings can be so simple: one of my friends recorded as her blessing today that her son did his homework without her having to remind him!

If you can read this book, you have sight. If you can tell a friend then you have a voice.

Count your blessings – the day is rich with them.

## How I Use My Blessings Book

I began keeping a 'blessings' book several years ago. It stayed in my bag at all times and when a blessing, a kindness, a funny story or something poignant registered with me, I would just jot it down in my book.

I now have a pile of them by my desk. Some are filled with cards from people we met on our travels, or slices of a magazine story, a photograph, some comments from the children, something copied off a friend's fridge magnet, a book I needed to buy... just pages of endless things that bring back a happy memory, or something I laughed at, or someone who touched my heart in some way.

I don't tidy the entries; I never use the pages in sequence; I don't make a special effort to use the same pen or pencil. They are just snapshots of happy memories (and in one case even a shopping list!). Yet whenever I open a page randomly, I enjoy reliving the experience, almost as if it had only just happened.

I would recommend you only use the book to record happy times. Keep the information that makes you feel good! Use **The Blessings Book** as your 'Good News Paper'! The content should bring a smile to your lips, act as a reminder of love and happiness captured and enable you to count your many blessings as they come to you.

*A blessing is...*

*...watching your children go forward
with wisdom because they weren't held back with fear.*

66 *Take nothing for granted.*
*Choose to have only*
*good days or great days.* 99

*A blessing...*

*...may not always be in the packaging you expect.*

*Happiness is a way of travel,*
*not the destination.*

Roy Goodman

*A blessing is...*

*...finding a moment to hear a sound, not just the traffic.*

*To thine own self be true*

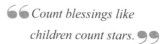

*Count blessings like children count stars.*

*A blessing is...*

*...a smile that starts on the lips and comes from the soul.*

*" Remember those who know the song
in your heart and remind
you of the words if you forget them. "*

*A blessing is...*

*...seeing that the world is "secrety and glittery",
even through the clouds.*

*" A child sees a
puddle as an opportunity,
not an obstacle. "*

*66 Dogs do the greatest good*
*for the fewest rewards. 99*

66 *Find peace with*
*who you are.*
*Only then will you be*
*content with*
*what you have.* 99

*A blessing is...*

*...remembering that your
husband put fuel in the car,
even if he didn't put the laundry
in the washing machine.*

**66** *One word of peace*
*is worth a thousand empty ones.* **99**

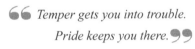

*Temper gets you into trouble.*
*Pride keeps you there.*

Anonymous

*A blessing is...*

*...seeing the richness in your life ~*
*despite your poor bank balance.*

*66 People are like stained glass windows:*
*they sparkle and shine when the sun is out,*
*but when the darkness sets in,*
*their true beauty is revealed*
*only if there is a light within. 99*

Elizabeth Kubler Ross

*❝Change the way you look
at things and the things
you look at will change.❞*

Dr Wayne Dyer

*What happens is not as important as
how you react to what happens.*

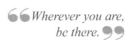

*Wherever you are,*
*be there.*

Confucius

*66 Cherish yesterday,*
*dream tomorrow,*
*live today. 99*

Richard Bach

66 *Examine what is said,*
*not who speaks.* 99

*A blessing is...*

*...allowing the work to pile up while you spend precious
time catching up with a friend.*

*A blessing is...*
*...sitting together in the middle of the sofa,*
*when there is plenty of room at both ends.*

*A blessing is...*

*...making someone smile today.*

*Heaven is a state of mind...*
*once you achieve it ~ you are there.*

*A blessing is...*
*...changing a moment of sadness into a*
*moment of reflection.*

*A blessing is...*

*...a friend who knows when to listen and when to speak.*

*A blessing is...*

*...living every day as if it is both your first and your last.*

*Man stands in his own shadow*
*and wonders why it's dark.*

Zen Proverb

*A blessing is...*

*...seeing each wrinkle as a trophy of a
life's experience and being proud of it!*

66 If fate throws a knife at you,
there are two ways of catching it:
by the blade or by the handle. 99

*A clever person solves a problem.*
*A wise person avoids it.*

Albert Einstein

*A blessing is...*

*...sharing the long drive home.*

*A blessing is...,*
*...not changing the past but shaping the future.*

*An eye for an eye
makes the world go blind.*

Mahatma Ghandi

*A blessing is...*

*...receiving a hand-written letter instead of an e-mail.*

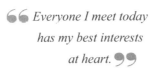

*Everyone I meet today has my best interests at heart.*

*A blessing is...*

*...when the chapters in
your love story keep being written.*

*A blessing is...*

*...hearing your mother's voice still guiding you.*

*www.theblessingsbook.com*

*A blessing is...*
*...finding the smile right under your nose ~*
*where you left it.*

66 *Teach your children* how *to think,*
*not* what *to think.* 99

*66 You can alter your life
if you alter your mind. 99*

William James

*A blessing is...*

*...when your teenager says "Let's get a movie"*
*rather than "Get out of my life".*

**66** *What lies before you, or behind you,*
*is nothing compared with what lies within you.* **99**

"When I first got my **Blessings Book**, Mum told us to write down all the people who loved us and nice things people had said to us. This was a start, and we could add into the book anything that made us smile or feel nice and happy. Like my Auntie buying me ice cream for breakfast one holiday.

Last term some people in my class were being very unkind to me. It made me very unhappy and I didn't want to go to school.

One night I took my **Blessings Book** and started to read the names of the people who really loved me, and the kind things people had said to me.

When the bullies were mean the next day, I could block out the things they said by thinking of all the nice things in my book that made me feel happy. I didn't give them any reactions and therefore they stopped bullying, and in fact now everyone is friends! I will write that in my book I think!"

*Molly, Wiltshire*

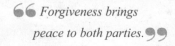

**66** *Forgiveness brings peace to both parties.* **99**

"I began to understand that counting your blessings is about more than just coping with unhappiness – it actually has the power to change your outlook on life.

If, every day, whether life is good or bad, you make the resolution to find one thing to be happy about – to feel blessed – and to write it down, it will not be long before you have a long list of joyful moments. But be aware: this can become addictive, and you will find yourself waking every morning remembering your blessings – and indeed counting them!"

*Hilary, Spain*


"Last year I started to get to know a boy I really liked. We spent some great times together laughing and chatting, and even kissing. I was so happy I started to write down all the lovely moments in my book.

Recently, I realised that he may be interested in another girl. I was very sad and angry to know this. I found my **Blessings Book** and decided to read through all the lovely times we had shared, and I found myself smiling and feeling warm. It didn't mean that the hurt was going away, but it did bring me some happiness and made me smile, instead of feeling sad."

*Eline, Belgium*